I'm Not Eighteen

Female Edition

Jean Dawn Leigh

jadie BOOKS

Published by
Jadie Books Limited 2007

Copyright © Jean Dawn Leigh 2007

ISBN 978-0-9549354-6-7

Cover illustration by Ian West

Typesetting by Jake Adie

Printed & bound by
York Publishing Services Ltd
64 Hallfield Road
Layerthorpe
York
YO31 7ZQ

For the not so young,
not so grown up,
not so sure

Other Not Really Titles

I'm Not Really 18 (male edition)

I'm Not Really 30 (female edition)

I'm Not Really 30 (male edition)

I'm Not Really 40 (female edition)

I'm Not Really 40 (male edition)

I'm Not Really 50 (female edition)

I'm Not Really 50 (male edition)

I'm Not Really 60 (female edition)

I'm Not Really 60 (male edition)

I'm Not Really Pregnant

I'm Not Really Getting Married

I'm Not Really Moving House

I'm Not Really Retiring

It's Not Really Christmas

Me Eighteen?

Now, hold on a minute. Let me go through this once more. Doesn't seem to add up properly no matter how many times I go over it. Right, one more time, zero plus seventeen add one equals . . . Oh, God, whichever way I try it, it still goes wrong. Still comes to eighteen. But eighteen's impossible.

Look, I'm sorry about this, it's so rude of me. You see, I'm having a bit of a crisis here and don't quite know how to get out of it because, according to the basic rules of arithmetic, which I must confess is not one of my strong points, I'm about to become eighteen. Me? Eighteen? I can't be. There must be something wrong somewhere. I just know there is. Look, I guess this must seem a bit odd to you, what with me, a perfect stranger, talking a load of nonsense about some birthday or other but, let me tell you, this is not exactly easy for me either. I mean, it's me who it's happening to. Me, who's got a birthday round the corner and

doesn't know
which way to
turn.
The fact is, I
know I'm not
about to be
eighteen
because I'm not
old enough yet.
Simple as that.
Yeah, I know
what you're
thinking: why
doesn't
somebody send
for the men in
white coats, but
it wouldn't be so
funny if you
were in my
boots. I'm being

serious. Listen, I've known EYOs for years and they've always been different to me. More mature, more knowledgeable, more grown up. So grown up, in fact, that I wouldn't be surprised if some of them were well into their twenties by now. How am I going to compete with that, eh? I'm just a regular young teenage girl with no great ambition in life other than to, well, other than to just carry on being a teenager. So how can I be expected to deal with all this awful coming-of-age, EYO business? It's not fair, it really isn't. I haven't got the first clue what you're supposed to do when you come of age. It's the start of being an adult, isn't it? An adult? Me? This is absurd. Why is everybody doing this to me? And I'm not imagining it because I've caught snippets of secret conversations at home and at college and I'm sure they're all planning a celebration or something. Without even asking my permission.

They're probably assuming it's got nothing at all to do with me. Great! Nothing to do with me? Thanks very much! It's only *me* who's got to do the growing up, the adulting. Me who's, all of a sudden, got to start to behave in a grown-up, responsible kind of manner. That's all. Nothing for them to do except buy cards and presents. Well, if you ask me, I think it's a downright liberty. It should be *my* choice whether I want to be an adult or not, no one else's. Mine. Well, I didn't ask them to get involved, did I? Entirely their decision. So, they shouldn't be surprised if I decide to have nothing to do with it, should they? Why should I care? I'll go off to someplace else that day and then it won't be me who'll look the idiot, will it? They'll just have to stand around with red faces and celebrate all by themselves. I have no intention of becoming an EYO just because *they* think I should.Hmm, see how they'll like that.

I'm Not Really Eighteen

Oh, I don't wish to be mean about the whole thing but when they have a birthday I don't tell them how old they've got to be. In fact, I don't even know how old most of them are anyway. It's just basic courtesy, don't you think? It's not polite to dictate your opinions to others like that especially about someone's age.

Well, that's the way I see it and that's all there is to it. Anyway, even if I was qualified to be an EYO, I couldn't because I haven't got any EYO . . .

Clothes

You'd think I'd, at least, have a few items ready in the wardrobe for the big day, wouldn't you? I mean, I'd look a bit of an idiot dressed in my normal gear when I'm supposed to be all grown up. That is what it's all about, isn't it? Coming-of-age, growing up, don't they mean the same thing? Course they do. There're no two

ways about it; if
you want to be a
proper EYO you
have to wear
proper EYO
clothes. And
anyway, I
haven't got any
money to buy
any new clothes
and that's not
very grown up
either, is it?
Grown-ups
always have
money, don't
they? But, even
if I did have
some money I
couldn't really go
out into the sorts

of shops EYOs go to; I'd feel silly. Everyone would look at me. They'd wonder what I was doing there. They'd probably come up to me to ask me if I was lost or something. See if I could remember where I last saw my mummy and stick a lollipop in my mouth. Well, okay, that may be exaggerating a bit but you can see what I'm getting at, can't you? And another thing; EYOs don't need to wait until they have enough money to buy new clothes because they have credit cards instead. It's all part of being an EYO and it doesn't just help their cash flow it allows them to look really cool at the same time. When I offer a shop

assistant
ordinary money
to buy
something new
they probably
think my mum
gave it to me.
And they
wouldn't be
wrong, would
they? I'd only
have it because
I'd saved my
pocket money
and gone
without for
weeks on end. So
the assistant
would be right; it
would be from
my mum. But

mums don't give credit cards as pocket money, do they?, No, of course they don't. So it's obvious that plastic cards have more street cred than cash, isn't it? They automatically make you look grown up. That's all there is to it. And there's another thing: EYOs have to have spare clothes as well as regular ones.

You know, clothes that just hang up in the wardrobe for certain occasions. Occasions that don't occur if you're a non-EYO, yeah? Like job or university interviews. Right? Well everyone knows you can't turn up at one of those dressed like you're about to go to the pictures. You wouldn't stand a chance, would you? No, if you've got to sit in front of a couple of important people for half-an-hour and make a better impression than the previous candidate, you've got to be sure you wear the right gear, yeah? And that means just one thing, a suit, right? Well, there you are; how many of

those do you
think I own?
Right first time,
none. Never
owned one in my
life. Mum's got
some though.
But then she
would; she's a
veteran EYO
herself. An elder,
if you like.
Although, if I
walked out of
the house
wearing one of
hers I'd get
arrested because
the skirt would
be down around
my ankles. No, I

don't mean she wears longer skirts than me, the waistband would be round my ankles as well. Sorry Mum. But even if I did go and buy myself something new like that I still couldn't walk down the street in it. No way. My mates would never let me live it down. They'd make my life unbearable. No, if I ever get to being an EYO I'll be the first to know about it. It will just feel sort of natural, I'm sure. And their suits will probably look good on me then without anyone taking the pee. Yeah, I'll get there one day but I'm sure not ready yet. You see, it's much more than just clothes. EYOs do all sorts of things that are totally alien to younger people like me. For instance, what about . . .

I'm Not Really Eighteen

If you're an EYO you have to know all about politics. It's compulsory, I think. It must be because when you really reach eighteen, the government sends you things through the post with all kinds of information about a club, or something, that you become a member of. I think it's called The Electorate Club and you

can only join if you're an EYO. You get a special membership number that allows you free admission to the village hall every now and again. But, as far as I can make out, it's not a very well organized club. In fact, it's very badly organized. Well, it must be because they only hold meetings once a year. Or, maybe not even as regular as that. And the strange thing is, none of the members seem to like going anyway. I know that because I've watched them. None of them seems to be prepared to give it any more than a couple of minutes. That's all. Honest. Although you do have to hand it to the organizers for their patience

— they just sit it out no matter what. Really. They stay on until right late at night before giving it up as a bad job. Anyway, that's all I know about politics and, frankly, if the EYOs aren't interested I can't imagine it'll ever appeal to me. It just appears to be a load of fuss about nothing. You'd think with so little interest it would just

fizzle out
overnight but it
doesn't.
And look at the
newspapers. The
amount of space
they devote to
the subject.
Pages and pages
every day of the
week and even
more on
Sundays. And all
they ever seem
to talk about is
whether the club
leaders are
doing their job
properly.
Properly?
They're hardly

doing it at all.
And what's
more, there are
always dozens of
other people who
seem to think
they could do the
job better. Well,
as far as I'm
concerned,
anyone could do
a better job.
What's the
problem? I
mean, it's not as
if they're holding
events every
week, is it?
Making a mess
of that would be
easier to

I'm Not Really Eighteen

understand. But once every year or two? It's unbelievable. But you know what really gets me? Yeah? It's that all EYOs — even really old ones — think it's terribly important. You can tell that if you hear them talking about it amongst themselves. Dead serious they are. Really. And they have arguments about it and get aggressive towards each other. They do. And the leaders, well, what can you say? They even show television programmes about them when they get together at the club's headquarters in London. You should see the way they talk to each other. Use up all their energy so quickly they just end up falling asleep. You wouldn't believe it, would you? I can't imagine anything so trivial appealing to me if I ever become an EYO. Definitely not. In fact, I think I'll just return the membership card and say no thank you. Surely they'll have to appreciate I'll have more important things to do with my time. I mean, wouldn't they be better employed running the country or something? Well, anything really. Anything would be better than trying to run those stupid meetings. Still, it does keep them off the streets I suppose. Could get into all sorts of trouble there. And while we're on the subject of trouble, what

Politics?

about EYOs and

. . .

39

Sex?

Hang about, this one could be a bit tricky. Well, it's not the easiest thing to talk about, is it? Couldn't imagine, for instance, discussing it with my mum. She'd go mad if I even brought the matter up. And definitely not Dad. But then that's because he doesn't know anything about it. Well that's what Mum says.

It is a funny subject though, don't you think? I mean, from what I do know about it, it's got to be one of the most important things about humans, hasn't it? After all, there wouldn't be any of us around if we didn't do it. So, whether people talk about it or not, they're obviously still doing it, aren't they? Must be.

And quite often, I should imagine. So what's the big secret, eh? We're allowed to talk about everything else we do like watching TV or eating a meal or going out with friends. So, what's the big deal about sex? Anyway, makes no difference to me because what little Mum has said on the subject has been confined to forbidding me to even think about it. EYOs don't get dealt with like that, I'll bet. So, what chance have I got of being an EYO if Mum won't let me think about it? Let alone do it! I don't have any choice in the matter, simple as that. Mum knows best. But what I'd really like to know is, what has it got to do with her anyway? And she's not the only one; all my friends' mothers say exactly the same thing. They act as though they run the country. But then, in a way, I suppose they do because the government, who should be running the country, reckon you're up for it when you're sixteen. So what is it with my mum that makes her think she knows better than the government, eh? What sort of message is that to give to a daughter? Confusing or what? No, I can't see any point in even thinking about being an EYO if I'm not allowed to do EYO-type things. And it isn't as if I don't know anything about it because I do. In fact, I probably know a lot more about sex than Mum does because we learnt it properly at school. In the classroom, not the playground like she did. Not a lot of good learning it there, is there? I mean, you wouldn't be allowed to get a job as a nuclear physicist if you told them in the interview that you learned how to do it in the playground, would you? Of course you wouldn't. So why does Mum think she's an authority on a subject *she* learned that way? And what makes her think she was qualified to have me if she hadn't really studied the subject properly? *We* don't do that, we have to take tests on it in class. Mind you, we did seem to know a lot about it before we even went to the first lesson. More than we knew about algebra. Lots more. It's strange though because no one I know ever wants to do algebra when they're outside of school but . . . no, perhaps I shouldn't go into that. You never know if Mum might find this book somewhere, do you? 'Hi Mum!'

(Just in case.) No, I'm afraid EYOdom is out of the question for the time-being. Besides, I'm not so sure it isn't more fun like this anyway. You know, *not* being allowed to do it. Can't be as much fun actually *being* allowed to do it, surely. Must be one of the great disadvantages of being an EYO, don't you think? And another

thing, what
about EYOs and
their . . .

Holidays?

Ehm? What about going away as an EYO? That must be different as well. Similar, in a way to sex, I should think. Well, insofar as being allowed to go is concerned. I have to suffer the embarrassment of going with Mum and Dad. Can you imagine? I mean, what do they think I want to do that for? Really? If I'm lucky, they let me take a friend with me. A *female* friend. Big deal. And what do you think my friends think about that? If *I* don't want their company why would one of my mates want it? Aren't they just impossible? Don't they remember being young themselves? Surely they didn't enjoy lying on the beach with Grandma and Grandpa. That would have been even worse. And you know their reason for not letting me go away without them? Yeah? Have a guess. Oh, all right, I'll tell you; they think I wouldn't be responsible. Me? Responsible? Mmm, I suppose they do have a point. Don't reckon I would be very trustworthy come to think of it. No, I don't mean in a calculating sort of way. Definitely not. And I don't think that's what they mean either. No, what I'd probably do is get on the wrong plane. Or not get on a plane at all. You know, get waylaid in one of those shops at the airport and miss my flight call. I would. That's just the sort of thing I'd do. Or forget where the hotel was and spend the night on the beach or something. And, of course, EYOs wouldn't do anything like that, would they? They're grown-ups after all. They'd take things much more seriously and listen out for the announcement over the Tannoy while they held a little piece of paper in their hand with the flight number on it. Mmm, I can imagine EYOs doing things like that. God, Mum's going to go mad when she finds out that I'm not going to be an EYO after all. She's probably made all sorts of plans for her and

Dad. Like just two holiday tickets maybe. Yeah, I can imagine her thinking I'm going to just turn into one as soon as my birthday arrives. I can really. It's just the sort of thing she'd think. Oh dear. What am I going to say to her? What am I going to say about the holiday? Can't just wait until the day comes and sound surprised when she calls upstairs to say goodbye. No, I can't do that, it'd be upsetting. I mean, I know I don't want to go with them but I do still want them to want me to. Well, it's natural, isn't it? Going to be in a bit of a fix. Not responsible enough to go alone and not wanted by my mum and dad.

What am I going to do? This not being eighteen stuff is not going to be at all easy to deal with. Suppose I'll be better off just staying at home. Untrustworthy and unwanted. Perhaps I'd better reconsider this whole EYO business. See if I can somehow pull it off after all. Might be possible. Ehm, let's have a look at another aspect of being an EYO. How about their . . .

I'm Not Really Eighteen

Work?

Doesn't seem to be any way out of this one if you get to be an EYO. If you don't go to uni you have to get a full-time job and if you do go you have to get a part-time one. Which means, if I'm ready to be eighteen, I'm ready to go to work. Well, I'm not. And, what's more, I can't imagine there's an employer out there who'd think I'd be of any help. Because I wouldn't. Besides, I'm much too young to be an employee. Employees are older types of people. I'd never pass as a worker at my age. I'd just look ridiculous. Can you seriously imagine me walking into an office building to start my first day at work? That's if I actually managed to find the place without Mum coming as well. Which is highly doubtful. But if I was lucky enough to get there and even find my way past the receptionist on the ground floor I'd never be able to make it to the office. No way. Somebody in the lift on the way up would definitely take my hand and lead me safely along the corridor to the crèche. Seeing that no harm came to me on the way. They would, really. How embarrassing. Turning up for my first day at the office in my smart new two-piece that Mum bought me and spending the whole day building Lego models. And, knowing me, once I'd found there was no way I was going to persuade Miss that I should really be working in Mr. Goodchild's office, I'd most likely take my jacket off, forget all about the job and begin to have a great time playing with all the other children. With the odd argument thrown in of course. It'd be much more fun than working. Trouble is, people would start getting suspicious when I was the only one at lunch-time without a mum. That would make me feel a bit uncomfortable especially when Miss started feeling sorry for me and decided to put a message out on the Tannoy while I was munching away at her jam sandwiches. What a way to begin a career. And can you picture the moment when Mr. Goodchild heard my name over the public address system? And the look on his face when he came down to collect me? How would I explain my way out of that one? He'd probably take one look at the chocolate biscuit

in my right hand
and the half-
built Lego
tractor in my left
and storm off
fuming in the
direction of the
Human
Resources office.
And, as if that
wouldn't be bad
enough, just
think what Mum
would say when
she got a phone
call from Miss at
five o'clock
asking her to
come and collect
me. And to make
sure she brought

a warm jumper because I'd got chocolate all over my new jacket. She'd hit the roof. Honest. How could I ever go for another job after that? I mean, what sort of reference would I get from Mr. Goodchild? *"Messy worker but makes fairly good Lego tractors"* is not exactly the most inspiring recommendation one can imagine handing to a prospective employer, is it? No, like it or not, it's going to be a good few years before I'm ready to be an EYO. Just have to find some way of occupying myself in the meantime. But, there's no harm in me acquainting myself with their general way of life, is there? You never know, it could help speed up the process. Maybe I should take a look at some other things they do. Their attitude, for example, towards . . .

Well, things must change in that direction too, surely. When you become an EYO you leave all your old school friends behind and meet a whole new bunch of people, don't you? Things on the social front begin to take on a completely new complexion. I mean, the relationships you had at

school, no matter how good they were to start with, will inevitably have become a bit stale. A bit past their 'sell-by' date, so to speak. When you've been spending every minute of every day with the same faces between the ages of eleven and seventeen there's little you can do, for instance, to enhance your identity if you feel it's ready for some subtle mutating. And after all those years it certainly will be, don't you think? School friends are going to be the last people on earth, well apart from Mum and Dad I suppose, who you'll stand any chance of impressing for God's sake. So, the onset of EYOdom must be an ideal time to make any necessary adjustments. Hairstyles, deportment, dress, make-up etc. You could even carry out some minor alterations to your voice, couldn't you? Like, maybe, losing just the right amount of your local accent to lend a certain sophistication, and mystique to your new identity. No one would be any the wiser because they'd know absolutely nothing about your past. Or your embarrassing performance in your biology examinations. Even your family (who you may feel it is particularly wise to keep quiet about). Yes, you will have an opportunity to totally re-invent yourself. Into whatever you feel most suits you. Just pick a character out of a magazine or off the telly and carve out a whole new image for yourself. And, you never know, some of their success could rub off on you. That wouldn't be bad, would it? But, of course, it's precisely what all your new acquaintances

will also have
done. They'll all
have access to
similar mags
and TV progs
and very likely
be impressed by
the self-same
icons. And the
net result could
be that no one
really knows
anyone properly.
Just their new,
carefully
adjusted
personas. A few
will remind you
of supermodels,
others, screen
stars while the

majority will just be dead-ringers for whoever happens to be topping the charts at the time. Could end up taking part in the biggest fancy-dress party ever held. In fact, the whole lot of them would probably stand a higher-than-evens chance of being joint, outright winners on that look-a-like, TV talent programme where you have to go into a room full of smoke to get changed. Know the one? (One way of ensuring privacy when you have to get your kit off, I suppose.) But I'm still sort of happy with the way I look now. And the way I talk. I know it would be nice to change things a bit but I really don't think I could pull it off. Well, not yet anyway. I'd probably find myself at some posh function where all these smart, re-invented people are impressing each other with their new images and look down to discover that, beneath my new sexy, see-through, silk cami, I'd forgotten to take off my, *'I'm a Burger-Bar kid'* fluorescent-yellow tee-shirt. That's just the sort of thing I'd do, really. The whole idea is just out of the question at the moment. I'm going to have to bide my time until I'm ready to get these things right. Carry on with life as a pre-EYO doing pre-EYO sorts of things. You know, I wouldn't be suprised if they didn't have a

whole different
approach to their
. . .

Well, why not? It wouldn't be unreasonable, would it? I mean, if an EYO occupied herself in her spare time by doing the sorts of things I do in my spare time she'd lose all her EYO credibility, wouldn't she? Cos when I get a moment to myself I, well, I, ehm . . . well, I can't quite think what I get up to if I'm totally

honest. I don't go horse riding anymore. And I haven't touched the piano for ages, thank God. What with all those stupid scales and finger exercises that boring old music teacher used to get me to do two million times a day. What was she like. Did she seriously think I'd end up on MTV backing some mega-famous boy band playing like that? What planet was she on? And I can't remember how long it's been since I stopped having swimming lessons. Or ballet classes. So, where does that leave me on the hobbies front? Well, the truth is, I just don't seem to have any. Unless, maybe, I can count my collection of popstar posters. Got loads of them. Still not enough though. Want to cover all the walls in my bedroom. And the door. And the sides of the wardrobe.Yeah, why not?, that'll count as a hobby. Course it will. It's something I spend a lot of my time doing. And a lot of my time thinking about. Even when I'm not in my bedroom. Like when I'm in the middle of exams, or coming home from school on the bus, I can't get some of those images out of my mind. Especially the one where Jason has got his shirt off and the top buttons on his jeans are . . . no, perhaps this isn't the time or place. But you see what I mean? They're definitely not the kinds of things you'd be interested in if you were an EYO. Can you imagine a proper old-enough-to-vote/get-married/go-to-work type person having a bedroom that looked like mine? It's obvious EYOs don't see the world that way. They look at things much more seriously. Just the way life is, I suppose.

Must be, like, when you wake up on the morning of your eighteenth birthday the first thing you do is rip down all the posters, screw them up and chuck 'em in the bin. Before you get showered. Must be like that because, well, because Mum doesn't have any popstars on her bedroom walls. All she's got is a couple of

pictures of, oh, I
don't know,
flowers or
something.
Yeah, flowers.
All right, I know
she's not an
EYO but she
used to be one a
few years ago.
And I'm sure she
didn't have
flower pics all
round her
bedroom walls
before she
became an EYO.
Wouldn't have
been normal,
would it?
Unhealthy

really, if you think about it. I mean, if she didn't like looking at all that testosterone when she was thinking about the sorts of things I spend most of my time thinking about then I probably wouldn't be here anyway. If you get what I mean. Cos if all she cared about was pretty-pretty flower pictures when she was my age something would have been seriously wrong in the development department. And she'd never have been interested in Dad as well. But, of course, now she's got me and my little sis, there's no reason why she needs to be interested in popstar posters. (Or in Dad, I suppose.) All seems to fall into place, when you

think about it.
S'pose that's
why I want to
stick them up on
the wall and she
doesn't. Oh God,
what a dreadful
thought. Like, if
I was really
going to become
an EYO, I'd have
to stop looking at
the posters and,
well, sort of
start . . . Mm,
perhaps it's not
such a dreadful
thought after all.
I mean, if I
really am about
to become an

EYO then I wouldn't need the posters because I'd actually be up for . . . No, I'm getting carried away now. This can't really be happening to me. Can it?